C000134404

For my two good friends
Peter and Philippa Haining

Junior Social Security Minister Oliver Heald's anti-fraud campaign inviting the public to inform on benefit cheats via a new telephone hotline was denounced by the Opposition as a snoopers' charter.

'Damned cheek! I've just spotted those layabouts next door watching us through binoculars!' *5 August 1996*

Only 16 months after the £1 billion 'Phoneday', it was announced that there would be another massive shake-up in telephone dialling codes, leaving businesses with huge bills for new stationery and reprogramming computers.

'0206473289917355421986384433? No, you've got the wrong number. This is 020849378660021499218347366...hello, are you still there?' *6 August*

Analysis of a Martian meteorite by scientists from the US space agency NASA revealed micro-fossil remains which gave 'strong circumstantial evidence' of life on the planet more than three billion years ago.

'Okay. It's only circumstantial evidence, but let's take a vote. Hands up those who think there's life on Mars...' *8 August*

Coinciding with the opening of the film *Independence Day* – in which the world is theatened by aliens – US President Clinton pledged to launch an armada of spaceships to search for further evidence of life on Mars.

'Wonderful news, girls – the Yanks are coming!' *9 August*

31-year-old Mandy Allwood of Solihull, pregnant with eight babies and advised to abort some on health grounds, was offered up to £350,000 for her story by the *News of the World* in what many saw as a publicity circus.

'All agreed? We're being exploited for cynical commercial gain. On the count of three, EVERYBODY KICK LIKE HELL!' *13 August*

Postal workers voted to strike despite the threat of losing their monopoly of mail delivery. Meanwhile, there was renewed controversy about falling standards when A-level pass-rates reached a record of 85.5 per cent.

'Mr B. Cookson, 10 Acacia Gardens, who called me an ignorant four-eyed cretin for going on strike... your daughter was lousy at English, failed dismally at Maths and History...' *15 August*

46-year-old dog-trainer, Carol Brampton, was banned for five years by the Kennel Club after being found guilty of doping Chizzy, a rival breeder's dog, at the Chihuahua Club Championships in Lytham St Annes, Lancashire.

'He looks fit. A nice shiny coat, clear eyes. Now if you'll just reel him in we'd like to do a blood test…' *16 August*

There was much heated debate when it was revealed that two gay men in Edinburgh had paid a surrogate mother £10,000 to have a baby for them.

2 September

Public feelings ran high when two Liverpool drug barons who had turned 'supergrasses' were released after serving only three years of their 18-year sentences.

'Honestly, lads, it's terrible. The pub's empty, there's nobody to talk to. Grassing on all your friends can make you very lonely…' *3 September*

Hundreds of treasure-hunters scrambled up the 2000-foot Irish mountain Croaghaun on Achill Island, Co. Mayo, when it was revealed that a man had lost his £2 million jackpot-winning Lottery ticket there.

Translation: 'Get help quickly! My friend has swallowed a small, crumpled-up ticket with numbers on it…' *6 September*

In an attempt to curb Britain's increasing 'yob culture', it was announced that police would be given powers to confiscate alcohol from under-age drinkers in public places.

'Let's get this straight, Jarvis. We apprehend under-age drinkers, we confiscate their alcohol, then we take it all back to the station.' *9 September*

A 12-year-old boy applied to the European Commission of Human Rights to claim that his rights had been violated when his stepfather caned him for threatening to stab his younger brother with a kitchen knife.

'Before you decide what action to take over my smashing up your car, Father, I'd like you to meet my lawyer, my social worker and a bloke from the European Commission of Human Rights...' *10 September*

The Government reeled as Spanish fishermen sued for damages after being banned from British waters, and the EU decreed that Britain could not block foreign pornographic TV channels and threatened to impose a 48-hour working week.

'Don't want, don't want? – You're asking for a good smacking!' *12 September*

The co-pilot on a British Airways flight to Milan confessed to fellow crew-members at 33,000 feet that he was afraid of heights and the plane had to make a forced landing in France so that he could get medical treatment.

'You're doing fine, Captain. But don't look down. We're at approximately fifteen feet now...' *13 September*

In a scandal which rocked the Roman Catholic church, the Rt Rev. Roderick Wright, 56-year-old Bishop of Argyll and the Isles, went missing in the company of 40-year-old divorcee and mother-of-three, Mrs Kathleen McPhee.

'Mr and Mrs Smith...?' *16 September*

Old Labour stalwarts were shocked when Tony Blair declared that relations with business were 'at least as important' as those with the unions and failed to condemn a move to drop the word 'socialism' from Labour policy.

17 September

Cardinal Basil Hume, leader of the Roman Catholic Church in England and Wales, suggested on Radio 4's 'Today' programme that the rule on priesthood celibacy, adopted *c.*1700 years ago and made law in 1139, should be relaxed.

'Cardinal Hume is doing all he can. These new portable cold showers must be costing the Church a fortune.' *19 September*

A female detective constable was paid £150,000 'hush money' in a secret deal to drop her sex-discrimination claim against male colleagues in the Harrogate police force after an inquiry revealed bizarre initiation ceremonies.

'I'm sorry, we were right in the middle of one of our initiation ceremonies when we got your 999 call…' *20 September*

The influential 'Vets in Support of Change' group published a report calling for Britain's rigid quarantine laws to be scrapped and replaced with vaccinations, microchip identity tags and pet passports.

'He hates people laughing at his passport photograph.' *27 September*

Labour's pre-election conference opened in Blackpool. Meanwhile, in Southampton, the Princess Royal fired the starting-gun to launch the 10-month, 30,000-mile BT Global Challenge round-the-world yacht race.

'No need for homesickness, chaps. Throughout our journey I intend to keep you informed with news, views and in-depth analysis of the Labour and Tory party conferences...' *30 September*

As a tribute to 77-year-old Jimmy Hogg, who collapsed and died of a heart-attack whilst playing golf in Fife, Scotland, his four pensioner companions decided to continue the game, to the amazement of onlookers.

'Could you hurry it up a bit, vicar? There's a foursome waiting to play through.' *1 October*

After four years of marriage, 40-year-old American model Jerry Hall sued 52-year-old Rolling Stones singer Mick Jagger for divorce on grounds of repeated infidelities.

'He's old, he's mean, he's promiscuous. But when he sings "I can't get no satisfaction" I think oh, what the Hell!' *18 October*

British shipbuilders Vosper Thorneycroft announced that there had been ‘intense interest’ in their revolutionary new warship the *Sea Wraith* which employed ‘stealth’-type technology to make it virtually invisible to radar.

‘Tell the captain you’re sorry to interrupt his bath but we think we’ve spotted a design fault…’ *21 October*

Members of a miners' support group dug a hole in the lawn of Michael Heseltine's country house, Thenford Hall, Northamptonshire, in protest at his attempt to close 31 collieries when President of the Board of Trade.

'Remember that little hole those protesters dug in the garden on Sunday, Mr Heseltine, sir? I think they must have found something…' *22 October*

Health Secretary Stephen Dorrell's Primary Health Care Bill included plans to replace one-man GP practices with multi-medical centres based in supermarkets and shopping centres.

'Let's see – beans, tea, cornflakes, have Grandad's appendix removed, jam, fish-fingers, biscuits…' *24 October*

Education Secretary Gillian Shephard backed a crusade to bring back discipline and traditional family values in schools and to teach children basic good manners.

'Remember what we learned today – it's PLEASE can we have your handbag? and THANK YOU when we scarper...' *28 October*

Margaret Moore, 44-year-old secret lover of former Yorkshire cricket star Geoffrey Boycott, claimed the 56-year-old batsman had beaten her up in their hotel while they were on holiday together on the French Riviera.

'To be honest, Geoff, this isn't what I meant when I whispered in your ear about foreplay…' *29 October*

Scotland Yard was alerted when it was alleged that members of the SAS and the Parachute Regiment had been involved in the illegal sale of military weapons while organising war-game weekends for businessmen.

'I know one can make a nasty sore place with a knife and fork, Benskin. But where's your rifle?' *1 November*

In the light of increasing attacks by pupils on teachers, new public-opinion polls favoured the return of corporal punishment in schools, a view given the personal support of Home Secretary Michael Howard and other MPs.

'What utter nonsense! Why should the little hooligans be rewarded when they misbehave?' *4 November*

The Duchess of York courted further royal displeasure when, to counter serialisation of the revealing private diaries of her former aide and confidant, Dr Allan Starkie, she published her own candid memoirs, *My Story.*

'Super bonfire, Mother – did you remember to organise a Guy?' *5 November*

As Labour gained in the polls and John Major's position looked ever weaker, US President Bill Clinton swept back into the White House in a landslide election victory, despite scandals surrounding his private life.

'Gosh. Thanks for the advice, Bill. Chase women, get involved in shady financial deals, persuade Norma to tell fibs and take up the saxophone...' *7 November*

Media pundits revealed that Labour leader Tony Blair was beginning to thin on top and an article in the *Financial Times* claimed that he had also adopted a new hairstyle to woo women voters.

'Mr Blair, sir. This advice from a leading hair specialist to stand upside down every day with your head in a cow pat – I'm sure it's in John Major's writing.' *8 November*

Prime Minister John Major was angered when the European Court ruled that Britain must accept the Working Time Directive regarding a 48-hour maximum working week.

'Whoops! 48 hours…nearly breached Brussels regulations.' *14 November*

ITV axed the glamorous beach-based American TV soap 'Baywatch' – featuring beautiful lifeguards such as Pamela Anderson – after ratings plummeted.

'I'm sorry, Marjorie. You're doing your best but I'm still going to miss "Baywatch".' *15 November*

National Curriculum tests on eleven-year-olds revealed that nearly half were below standard in maths and most were below average in reading, writing and spelling. Two failed GCSE pupils later threatened to sue their schools.

'Meet my lawyer. I'm claiming compensation for stress, caused by the knowledge that I'm nearly eleven and I'm still a cretin.' *19 November*

As blizzards brought Britain to a standstill, there were heated exchanges in Parliament when a survey revealed that little progress had been made to honour the Government's promise to phase out mixed-sex hospital wards.

'Complaints, complaints! First it was about being in a mixed ward – now what?' *21 November*

After a report by the Audit Commission spelt out the enormous costs of rising juvenile crime in the UK, the Government announced that the electronic wrist-tag curfew system would be extended to offenders aged 10 to 15.

'Stop moaning. That nice policeman promised if you're good for a whole year he'll reduce the size of your tag.' *22 November*

Chancellor Kenneth Clarke's struggle to produce a vote-winning pre-election budget was blighted when 100 pages of his market-sensitive deliberations were leaked to the *Daily Mirror*.

'Free booze, free petrol, scrap income tax, holidays for all in Barbados? Dammit, Ken, you'll have to do better than that for us to win the election.' *27 November*

The Government introduced a plan to force foreign fishing-boats to have English-speaking crews in an attempt to stop 'quota-hopping' overseas vessels registered in Britain taking nearly 20 per cent of the UK's catch.

'Right, señores. First lesson: Useful phrases – slowly and clearly after me…' *28 November*

Brussels gave the go-ahead for the sale of unlabelled genetically modified products in the UK, despite a survey suggesting that 93 per cent of consumers wanted these so-called 'Frankenstein foods' to be clearly identified.

'Well, it didn't say anything on the wrapping about being genetically altered.' *5 December*

After *in vitro* fertilisation, 57-year-old Edith Jones gave birth to her own granddaughter in Darlington Memorial Hospital, Co. Durham, when her daughter was unable to conceive because of a medical condition.

'Of all the women you could have asked to act as a surrogate, you had to choose your mother!' *9 December*

Prime Minister John Major pleaded with rebel Tory Eurosceptics to back his 'wait and see' policy on a single European currency in a desperate bid to unify the party as it trailed 35 per cent behind Labour in the polls.

'Stop squabbling! As far as our future is concerned, if a wait-and-see policy is good enough for John Major, it's good enough for us...' *10 December*

Princess Diana turned up at a charity dinner in New York wearing a £10,000 midnight-blue satin dress trimmed with black lace, designed by John Galliano for Dior, which critics said resembled a nightie.

'Relax. It's the height of fashion. If Princess Diana can go out in her nightie, so can I.' *12 December*

Virgin tycoon Richard Branson's bid to fly around the globe in a giant propane-gas-powered hot-air balloon ended in failure when technical problems forced it to make an emergency landing in Algeria after only 21 hours.

'Hey, Ahmed, look what just fell out of the sky – Richard Branson's underpants!' *9 January 1997*

The soccer world was stunned when Kevin Keegan, the much-loved manager of Newcastle United, resigned suddenly. Meanwhile, a Mori poll and TV debate revealed that Prince Charles's public image had reached an all-time low.

'Why aye, bonny hinny. Me Mam and me Da' would be dead chuffed if ah wis tae becoom as popular as yon Kevin whatsisname…' *10 January*

Radio 1 disc-jockey Chris Evans, who had earlier submitted his resignation over working hours, was sacked from his £7000-a-day job two months before his notice expired when he failed to turn up to present his show.

'Stay cool, pop pickers. Chris Evans's replacement will be with you soon. Till then, a few of my favourites from 'ome. Let's get grooving with Vera Lynn…' *21 January*

Defence Secretary Michael Portillo drew up plans for a 'massive boost' to expand the recruitment of Army, Navy and Air Force Cadets amongst children aged 13 to 16.

'That's nice, dear. And what else did you learn at Mr Portillo's Cadets today?' *24 January*

Tony Blair attacked Tory plans to spend £60 million of tax-payers' money on a replacement for the royal yacht *Britannia,* calling the scheme a 'political stunt' and adding that a Labour government would not provide the cash.

'It's for you, Tony darling. I think it's about the Royals' new boat…' *27 January*

Health Secretary Stephen Dorrell pledged to put an end to mixed-sex wards in hospitals and mental homes.

'The men's wards are absolutely packed, so when we took out your appendix we did a sex-change operation too . . .' *28 January*

Princess Diana donated her 1981 wedding dress to the Victoria & Albert Museum and put up 65 of her most famous designer evening dresses for auction at Christie's to benefit AIDS and cancer charities.

See? All that money you spent on Princess Diana's old dress was worth it – everybody's staring.' *30 January*

29-year-old Noel Gallagher, guitarist and songwriter of the hugely successful pop group, Oasis, caused a furore when he said on BBC Radio 5 Live that taking drugs was just like having a cup of tea.

'Right, ladies, that settles it. Despite what Noel Gallagher says, for our future church flower-arrangement committee meetings we'll stick to tea...' *31 January*

Tory Eurosceptic Sir George Gardiner was deselected by his Reigate constituency for repeated criticisms of the Government. Meanwhile, anti-motorway campaigner 'Swampy' Hooper was arrested after a week underground in Devon.

'It's Sir George (call me Swampy) Gardiner, Inspector. He's dug a tunnel and he's not coming out till he's been reselected…' *3 February*

The Conservatives launched a nationwide poster campaign featuring a lion weeping a red tear, to symbolise Britain suffering under Labour's pro-Social Chapter employment policy, with the slogan 'New Labour – Euro Danger'.

'Great news, chaps. The Prime Minister loves the new poster.' *4 February*

Outraged military chiefs described Shadow Chancellor Gordon Brown's proposed pay-freeze for top brass and civil servants as 'mean and bad for morale' and likely to spark mass defections from the Services and Whitehall.

'All systems are go for Operation Shadow Chancellor, sir. He's just getting into the bath…' *6 February*

A book by Peter Watson, *Sotheby's: Inside Story,* and a documentary filmed for Channel 4's 'Dispatches' programme, revealed that Sotheby's had been engaged in the systematic smuggling of Old Master paintings from Italy.

'If Lot 22 looks a little crumpled, this is because our expert had it stuffed down his trousers as he came through Customs.' *7 February*

Former Archbishop of Canterbury, Lord Runcie, blamed 'happy-and-clappy, huggy-and-feely' services for the biggest collapse in Anglican congregations in 20 years. Meanwhile, Oasis star Liam Gallagher married Patsy Kensit.

'However, we will continue to provide young and trendy services, Liam. I do the happy-clappy section and our Mr Shuttleworth does the huggy-feely bit.' *10 February*

Home Secretary Michael Howard's Crime Bill, advocating tough mandatory sentences for criminals who make a career out of burglary or drug-dealing, went before the House of Lords.

'Before we decide if we're goin' to do your place over, milord, are you for or against the 'Ome Secretary's Crime Bill?' *12 February*

British Airways were flooded with telephone calls when an estimated 30 million people tried to book 190 seats on a Concorde flight to New York for £10 each in a special promotional offer.

'Moan, moan, moan! What did you expect for ten pounds?' *13 February*

On the eve of St Valentine's Day, England's football team suffered its first ever defeat at Wembley. Italy, wearing blue, beat the home side 1–0 in a critical World Cup qualifying match.

'When Mum whispered in your ear, "Roses are red, violets are blue, what are your thoughts turning to?", I don't think she meant England losing one–nil to Italy.' *14 February*

In the worst case of corruption in its history, a senior Inland Revenue official was jailed for taking bribes to fund a life of luxury. He also accepted the services of a call-girl paid for by wealthy businessmen.

'Not now, dearie. I'm doin' my income-tax returns.' *20 February*

46-year-old father-of-five, Dr John Browne, a popular Oxford GP, spent £9000 on a sex-change operation and wrote to his 15,000 patients saying that he would return as Dr Joanna Browne.

'When I said I'd prefer to be examined by a woman, I didn't mean you to go to such trouble, Doctor.' *21 February*

Dolly the Finn Dorset lamb hit the headlines when scientists at the Roslin Institute near Edinburgh revealed that she was the first exact twin of an adult sheep to be cloned from a single cell of her mother.

'Cloning smelly old sheep. What time do you call this? Your dinner's frizzled, you never ring…' *24 February*

After the public outcry over failures of justice such as the case of the Bridgewater Three, the Home Secretary announced that henceforth juries would be shown videos of all police interviews with defendants.

'... and now, jurors, we interrupt this interview to bring you news of the freshly ground taste and lip-smacking aroma of Gribley's Coffee, available now at...' *25 February*

Social Security Secretary Peter Lilley published a White Paper proposing that a spouse's pension fund should be split between the two parties in the event of a divorce.

'Let's see, what shall I do tomorrow? Have breakfast in bed, the house painted, a new dress, the garden dug over and receive a huge bunch of roses – or file for a divorce?' *27 February*

In an extraordinary move to save money, the Duchess of York and her two daughters left their £1500-a-week rented Surrey mansion and moved back into Prince Andrew's home, Sunninghill Park, in Berkshire.

'You look guilty. I hope you haven't been up to any of your moneymaking schemes while I've been out.' *28 February*

Faced with increasing hooliganism by the very young, Shadow Home Secretary Jack Straw proposed the abolition of the medieval legal defence of *doli incapax* which deems children aged between 10 and 13 'incapable of evil'.

'Here is a newsflash. In the Commons today the Shadow Home Secretary, Jack Straw, suddenly came out in boils, burst into flames and was carried away by a giant fruit bat...' *4 March*

Following an outbreak of deaths from the killer *E-coli* food bug in Scotland, Agriculture Minister Douglas Hogg was accused of suppressing a report criticising poor hygiene in Britain's abattoirs.

'Great news! I've heard the abattoir is filthy.' *7 March*

At a Glasgow conference of the Society for the Protection of Unborn Children it was announced that the Roman Catholic Church in Scotland would set up a fund offering cash rewards to pregnant mothers who refused abortion.

'So, Father. If you could spare a few quid for a poor, lost slip of a girl like me, I promise I won't have an abortion.' *10 March*

In an attempt to win pensioners' votes, a government-sponsored 'partnership' insurance scheme was introduced so that the elderly wouldn't need to sell their property to pay for the costs of long-term residential care.

'That's right, they're both pretty ancient. How much will it cost to ensure they can go into residential care and leave the house to their kids?' *11 March*

John Major intervened personally in the food-safety row after disregarded letters from the Association of Meat Inspectors, warning Ministers that the UK's dirty abattoirs were a potential hygiene 'time-bomb', were published.

'Something's going on. I heard that only a few days ago this place was filthy.' *13 March*

There was considerable debate when an American prison ship, renamed HMP *Weare*, arrived from New York. Five storeys high, 300 feet long and capable of holding 500 convicts, its intended site was Portland Harbour, Dorset.

'We suspect Murphy on "D" deck has started a tunnel, Governor…' *14 March*

John Major decided on a 1 May poll, thereby beginning the longest general election campaign in Britain this century. He also pledged to take part in the first ever US-style TV confrontation between party leaders.

'I've had that dream again, Norma. Where I'm on TV, slugging it out with Tony Blair...' *17 March*

Controversy raged as censors gave an '18' certificate to David Cronenberg's uncut 'sex and wrecks' film *Crash*. Westminster Council nevertheless banned it from all West End cinemas and many other authorities followed suit.

'Another headache? You've always got a headache!' *20 March*

An autograph-hunter claimed she was hit by England football star, Paul Gascoigne. Meanwhile, riot police fired tear-gas and rubber bullets at Manchester United fans in Portugal after a Champions League match against Porto.

'Guess what? While you were in Portugal getting shot at by the police, I got Gazza's autograph.'

21 March

Parents protested and two County Commissioners threatened to resign when the Scout Association decided to accept homosexuals, former drug-addicts and ex-convicts as scoutmasters under a new 'equal opportunities' directive.

'All together now... campfire's burning, campfire's burning, draw nearer, draw nearer...' *24 March*

A mass breakout of top IRA terrorists held in Belfast's high-security Maze Prison was narrowly avoided when a 90-foot tunnel was discovered when it accidentally collapsed.

'A tunnel? We wondered what that thing was!' *26 March*

The Tory election campaign suffered a double blow when former Northern Ireland Minister Tim Smith resigned over the cash-for-questions affair and Kent MP Piers Merchant became involved in a sex scandal with a 17-year-old girl.

'No, I'm not canvassing. I want to move in.' *28 March*

As politicians fought for public attention over the Easter weekend, the new independent TV station, Channel 5, went on air. Unfortunately, one in three viewers could not receive it at all and 40 per cent had poor reception.

'No politics, no sleaze, no picture. I think Channel 5 is wonderful!' *31 March*

One of the centrepieces of the Tory election manifesto was a plan to transfer personal tax allowances to spouses who give up work in order to bring up children or take care of elderly or sick relatives.

'So with personal allowances standing at £4045 a year and standard tax at 23p in the pound it means a cash bonus of £17.89 a week if one of your parents gives up work to look after you. Will you explain that to them when they get home?' *3 April*

An estimated 70,000 people were evacuated from Aintree racecourse when a coded bomb-alert from the IRA was received. As a result, the 150th Grand National was postponed until the following Monday.

'Here he comes now...placed a £10,000 bet that the National would be postponed 'til Monday.' *7 April*

41-year-old Clapham sculptor Anthony-Noel Kelly, a cousin of the Duke of Norfolk, was arrested when human remains used to make his macabre art figures were found in the grounds of his family home, Romden Castle, Kent.

'I have a message from your late grandfather, Bernard. He says he's hanging on an art-gallery wall in Clapham, priced £250.75p or near offer.' *11 April*

British defending champion Nick Faldo crashed out of the US Masters Golf Championships in Augusta, Georgia, which were won by 21-year-old Tiger Woods. The winner of the 1997 London Marathon was Portugal's Antonio Pinto.

'Daddy would've been here hours ago but he didn't want to miss the golf.' *14 April*

Having himself become a father at the age of 14, Warwickshire digger-driver Dale Wright (29) became Britain's youngest grandfather when his 14-year-old son, Stephen, sired a daughter.

'Hello, *Guinness Book of Records*?' *15 April*

In an out-of-court settlement, two major US tobacco companies agreed to set up a £188 billion medical fund to care for victims of smoking-related diseases for 25 years in return for immunity from liability suits.

'Okay. I feel sick. Let's go and sue the tobacco companies.' *18 April*

When asked on the Internet's 'Microsoft News' if she had ever smoked cannabis, Labour MP Clare Short declined to answer because then everyone on Labour's front bench would be asked, 'And then some will have to confess or lie.'

'Edmond, there's a gentleman lying in our azaleas wishing to know if we intend to spliff up on the grass, tune in and freak out with Labour on May 1st.' *21 April*

Only days before the election, former Food Minister Edwina Currie, MP for Derbyshire South, was rounded on by her conservative colleagues when she predicted a Labour landslide of over 100 seats and blamed John Major.

'The Prime Minister won't be long. He's just nipped out for a Currie.' *28 April*

When Norwegian scientists claimed that a golden retriever had died from BSE after eating imported British dog food, the Government confirmed that a report on 'mad cow disease' in pets had been kept secret for six years.

'I think he wants to go walkies.' *29 April*

Having suffered a record-breaking 45 days of electioneering, the nation finally went to the polls.

'Wake up. It's May 1st. We can go down now.' *1 May*

New Labour won a resounding victory and were returned to Parliament with a majority of 179. Tony and Cherie Blair, together with their three children – Euan (13), Nicky (11) and Kathryn (9) – moved into 10 Downing Street.

'I dunno. Since he became Prime Minister the bedtime stories just haven't been the same.' *6 May*

As Labour prepared to write their first Queen's Speech for 18 years, a special photo-call of the party's 101 women MPs – dubbed 'Blair's Babes' – was held on the steps of Church House, Westminster.

'I approve of most of it, Mr Blair. But I think we'll continue to call it The Queen's Speech.' *8 May*

There was a public outcry when a Church Commissioners' report revealed that an extra £500,000 had been spent on bishops' palaces while clergy salaries were being cut and higher donations were being demanded of parishioners.

'Dearly beloved. Today's collection will go towards the upkeep of the Bishop's Palace. So – hands against the wall, feet apart…' *9 May*

In New York, IBM's chess-playing computer, 'Deep Blue', became the first machine to beat a reigning world champion in a classical match when it defeated 34-year-old Russian grandmaster, Garry Kasparov.

'Look, Buddy. I don't care who you just beat at chess. Go home, you've had enough.' *13 May*

Her Majesty delivered the first Queen's Speech of the new Parliament. Gordon Brown also made his first speech as Chancellor at the Mansion House and broke with tradition by not wearing white tie and tails.

'... then just as we were leaving, what a relief – Tony whispered in my ear, "There's no need to dress quite so formally in future." ' *15 May*

31-year-old surrogate mother, Karen Roche, who claimed to have aborted the baby she was carrying for a Dutch couple, admitted that she had lied and said that she wanted to keep the child after all.

'Well, he's not exactly a baby, but we heard you were desperate.' *16 May*

Two weeks after Manchester United won the Premier League, the team's star striker, Eric Cantona – who had once karate-kicked an insulting Crystal Palace supporter – announced his retirement as a professional footballer.

'It's only a game of dominoes, Mr Cantona!' *19 May*

A Government announcement that sports sponsorship by tobacco companies was to cease meant that motor-racing, rugby, snooker, darts, golf and fishing championships would have to look elsewhere for some £8 billion a year.

'Strange, we just don't seem able to attract the big names since Dunhill was forced to pull out.' *20 May*

For the first time in its history, the British Secret Service department, MI5, placed advertisements for new Intelligence officers in the Situations Vacant column of national newspapers.

'The name's Sludgebucket... Kevin Sludgebucket.' *22 May*

It was reported in the *New Scientist* that geneticists studying nematode worms at University College, London, had discovered that celibate males live longer than promiscuous ones, leading to speculation about humans.

'Hello, Samaritans? I'm thinking of ending it all.' *23 May*

After talking tough on Europe a month before the important EU summit in Amsterdam, Tony Blair invited the hardline former Tory premier, Margaret Thatcher, to No. 10 for advice in an hour-long brainstorming session.

'No, no, Prime Minister. Knee in groin too slow, right arm bent, no follow-through. A Euro Minister would've seen that coming a mile off.' *26 May*

Two homosexual men who had been rejected as potential foster parents caused an uproar when they demanded equal rights of surrogacy as heterosexuals and advertised for a lesbian couple who would share a baby with them.

'Sorry to bother you, Alice. My Norman's getting ever so broody. We wondered if you'd do us a favour…' *29 May*

John Major stood down as leader of the Conservative Party. Contenders for the post included Kenneth Clarke, Stephen Dorrell, Michael Howard, Peter Lilley and the 36-year-old former Welsh Secretary, William Hague.

'Be warned. When we have elected our new leader, he's going to give you such a nasty nip on the ankle!' *2 June*

It was announced that the cricket-loving former Prime Minister, John Major, would be a guest presenter on BBC Radio 4's 'Test Match Special' programme during the Benson & Hedges Cup Final.

'... and so, humiliated and defeated, the batsman sadly trudges away from his shattered stumps, his dreams of a long innings ended. My heart goes out to him, a nation weeps...' *5 June*

Deputy PM John Prescott and Heritage Secretary Chris Smith attacked the fat cats running the Lottery and the recently privatised utilities as profits continued to soar while services dwindled and household bills increased.

THE GRAVY TRAIN

6 June

When Kenneth Clarke won the first Tory leadership ballot, Peter Lilley and Michael Howard withdrew and backed William Hague. Meanwhile, French immigration officers arrested a Eurotunnel worker for avoiding National Service.

'I assure you, *mon ami.* His name's William le Hague and he's over here trying to dodge French National Service...' *12 June*

Support fell away from Kenneth Clarke, MP for Rushcliffe, Nottinghamshire, after he made a deal with right-winger John Redwood, and William Hague won the Tory leadership contest, making him the youngest leader of any party this century.

'It's William Hague. Let the festivities begin!' *20 June*

The US space-probe, *Pathfinder*, landed on Mars and released a six-wheeled vehicle which transmitted TV pictures of the planet. Back on earth, Cherie Blair took her hairdresser to the G7 world leaders' summit in Denver at a cost of £2000.

'Stop moaning. You're just about to appear on Earth's TV screens, where £2000 for a hairdo is peanuts.' *7 July*

Peace talks between British Airways and the Transport & General Workers' Union over pay and conditions ended in deadlock and led to the first of a series of strikes by 7500 cabin-crew members.

'Thank you for flying British Airways. I don't know nothin' about safety procedure, there ain't no duty-frees, but does anybody fancy an 'ot dog?' *8 July*

40-year-old Massachusetts mother-of-three, Carolyn Abagis, produced a housework-linked fitness video, 'Lean-n-Clean', after losing four stone in six months by doing exercises while carrying out normal domestic chores.

'I don't like to disturb her right now – she's going for the burn.' *10 July*

When the Prime Minister said that he would back a Private Member's Bill to ban fox-hunting with hounds, more than 100,000 protesters from all walks of life rallied in Hyde Park to defend the rights of country people.

'... and finally, before they get back from Hyde Park, I'd like to thank you all for attending this rally which I'm sure you'll agree has been well worth while.' *11 July*

As an anti-smoking summit debated raising the age for buying cigarettes to that for purchasing alcohol, the Government backed down in its opposition to an EU ruling on lowering the age of consent for homosexuals to 16.

'Wonderful news, darling. Tony Blair's policies are working – our Kevin's given up smoking.' *15 July*

Glenn Watts, a 24-year-old plumber from Haverhill, Suffolk, who had once been jailed for his part in an armed robbery on a post office, scooped £2.6 million in a midweek Lottery jackpot.

'Hang on, I've changed my mind.' *17 July*

The 126th Open Golf Championship at Royal Troon was won by 25-year-old Texan, Justin Leonard.

'FORE!' *21 July*

Education Secretary David Blunkett announced the expansion of the student loan scheme, the complete phasing out of student grants and the introduction of means-tested tuition fees costing as much as £1000 a year.

'Morning, Dad.' *22 July*

Labour's long-awaited plans for Scottish devolution were revealed. If a referendum proved positive, the first election of 129 members to an independent Parliament in Edinburgh would take place in the spring of 1999.

'Slow down. I think you've just driven straight through Scottish Customs.' *25 July*

Deputy Prime Minister John Prescott shelved plans to widen the M25, axed the proposed Salisbury bypass and other projects but gave the go-ahead to the Birmingham North Relief Road, the first modern private toll route.

'I have wonderful news for you – John Prescott's cancelled it.' *29 July*

Local officials were outraged when a bright red 'Love Bus' run by a youth charity toured Cornwall's holiday beaches, giving sex advice and handing out free condoms to children as young as 13.

'Ah, listen, children. Ting-a-ling, ting-a-ling – Who'd like an ice cream?' *31 July*

A leading National Hunt trainer announced that he was experimenting with Australian-designed 'nappies' for his racehorses in an effort to save on the huge labour and bedding costs resulting from mucking out stables.

'He absolutely refuses the humiliation of wearing a nappy.' *1 August*

Faced with exposure by a Sunday newspaper, 51-year-old Foreign Secretary and father of two, Robin Cook, admitted adultery with his political secretary and announced that he would leave his wife of 28 years.

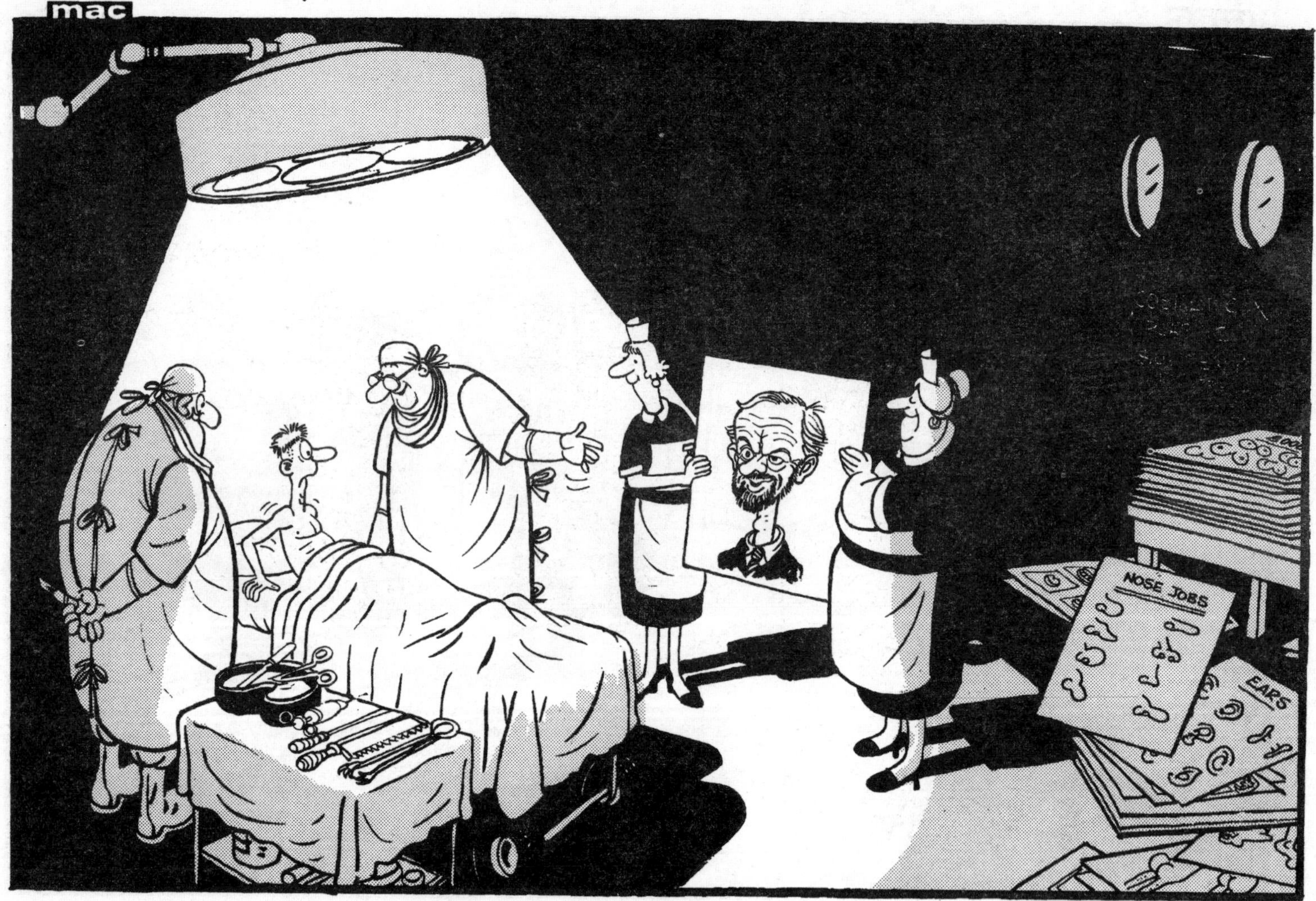

'You want to look sexy and attract females? It's expensive, but this look is driving women wild at the moment.' *4 August*

Fully recovered from her hip operation, the 97-year-old Queen Mother greeted 3000 well-wishers as the band played 'Happy Birthday' outside her London home, Clarence House.

'So I said, "Look, Mother, at 97 you've got most things and done practically everything. What would you like for a present?"' *5 August*

Princess Diana's public image continued to soar as she took her anti-landmine campaign to Bosnia.

'We can't let Diana hog all the publicity, Camilla darling. So I've arranged for you to be parachuted into Rwanda.' *7 August*

Italian paparazzi revealed that Princess Diana's new love was Dodi Fayed, 41-year-old millionaire film-producer son of Harrods boss, Mohamed Al Fayed. The couple were spotted on holiday together in the Mediterranean.

'Go on, give her a call. Just say: "I too am the son of a shop-owner. Free, unattached and considering a week in Skegness."' *8 August*

The Government announced that synthetic alternatives were being sought to replace Guards' bearskin hats. Meanwhile, a woman from Wigan received a three-inch burn when her Marks & Spencer's knickers ignited spontaneously.

'Not only the bearskin, Sarge. Traces of sheep were found in the jacket, a poor cow had to be sacrificed for the boots and I was a bit scared my Marks & Spencer underpants might spontaneously combust.' *15 August*